Competency Reading Series

Examining Words and Their Meanings

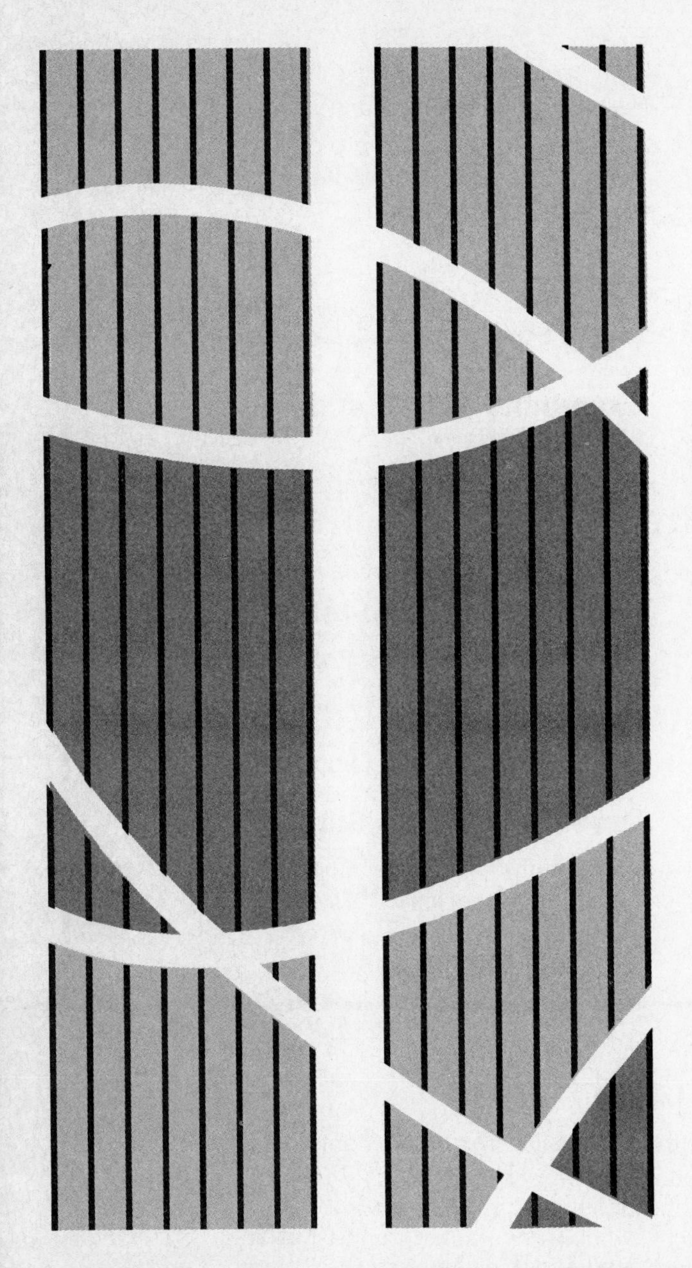

Don Barnes
Jerry Brown
Arlene Burgdorf

Illustrated by Michael Krone

Steck-Vaughn Company
Austin, Texas

About the Authors

Dr. Don Barnes received his doctorate in education from the University of Northern Colorado. Dr. Barnes is professor of education at Ball State University. He taught in various public schools and universities before joining Ball State in 1956. Dr. Barnes is a member of the American Education Research Association, the Commission of Higher Education of the State of Indiana, the Ohio Valley Philosophical Association, the Midwest Philosophy of Education Association, and many others. He has published materials previously in Great Britain, Sweden, Germany, Italy, Australia, and India.

Dr. Jerry Brown received his doctorate in education from UCLA. He joined the faculty of Indiana University and was associate director of its Laboratory for Educational Development. In 1974 Dr. Brown moved to the Agency for Instructional Television after having served as a consultant for the instructional design of AIT's Emmy award-winning *Inside/Out* series. He now serves as AIT's director of instructional design and as a project officer for the Skills Essential to Learning Project.

Dr. Arlene Burgdorf received her doctorate in elementary education from Ball State University. Dr. Burgdorf is a former resource consultant for the Hammond, Indiana, Public Schools. She has taught at all levels from kindergarten to university graduate programs, and she has served as a principal of an elementary school. Dr. Burgdorf has prepared numerous instructional materials in reading which have been widely used.

Competency Reading Series

Judging and Arranging Information
Drawing Conclusions
Summarizing Information
Identifying the Main Idea

Finding Patterns
Understanding Sequences
Predicting Outcomes

Analyzing Content
Recalling Details
Judging Between Fact and Opinion
Distinguishing Between Real and Fanciful

Examining Words and Their Meanings
Vocabulary Development
Using Context Clues
Using Structural Analysis

Interpreting Visual Information
Using Directional Signs, Notices, and Directories
Interpreting Maps
Interpreting Graphs, Charts, and Tables

Developing Basic Study Skills
Using Encyclopedias, Telephone Directories, and Dictionaries
Using Parts of Books
Following Directions

ISBN 0-8114-0959-7

 Printed and bound in the United States of America.

6 7 8 9 0 HG 92 91

Contents

Vocabulary Development

Using Context Clues

Using Structural Analysis

VOCABULARY DEVELOPMENT

Colossus of Rhodes

This statue was one of the seven wonders of the ancient world. It was built to celebrate the end of a long battle. It was made of bronze. The statue was reinforced with iron and weighted with stone. It took twelve years to finish the huge figure. The Colossus was completed in the year 280 B.C. It stood near the harbor at Rhodes.

In 225 B.C., the statue cracked at the knee. The following year, the statue was destroyed by an earthquake. In 653 A.D., the bronze in the statue was hauled away and sold for scrap. It is said that more than one hundred camels were used to carry off these bronze pieces. And it took these camels more than nine hundred trips to complete their work. Finally, it was done. The once mighty Colossus was no more.

Culver Pictures

A. Write a word or phrase that has the *same* meaning for each word below.

1. battle ______________
2. long ______________
3. reinforced ______________
4. almost ______________
5. scrap ______________
6. huge ______________
7. (to) haul ______________
8. (to) celebrate ______________

B. Write a word or phrase that has the *opposite* meaning for each word below.

1. (to) build ______________
2. (to) finish ______________
3. ancient ______________
4. colossal ______________

A Lasting Memorial

Emma Lazarus was the daughter of Jewish immigrants. There were six girls in the family. But Emma was her father's favorite.

Emma was wealthy. She lived in New York City. She never married. Her days were spent reading. She was often moody. She was able to express her moods with words. Those words became poems. Other poets knew her work and encouraged her. Several magazines published both her poems and her essays.

In 1885, the boxes containing the parts to the Statue of Liberty arrived in New York. This statue was a gift from France to America. A fitting base was needed for this symbol of freedom. Many people worked to raise money for the base. To inspire these efforts, Emma wrote a poem. The poem put into words what the statue stood for.

The New-York Historical Society, New York City

Port Authority of New York

In 1886 the statue was complete. Emma's poem was engraved on its pedestal. The most famous part is

> Give me your tired, your poor,
> Your huddled masses yearning to breathe free,
> The wretched refuse of your teeming shore,
> Send these, the homeless, tempest-tossed to me.
> I lift my lamp beside the golden door!

These words serve as a lasting monument to the woman who wrote them.

A. Word choice is important in writing. It is very important when writing poetry. Using other words might change the feeling you can get from a poem. Write a word that has the same meaning as each of the words below. All are taken from Emma Lazarus's poem.

1. tired ______________________
2. huddled ______________________
3. yearning ______________________
4. wretched ______________________
5. refuse ______________________
6. teeming ______________________
7. tempest ______________________
8. lift ______________________

B. Rewrite Emma's poem. Use your answers in Part A instead of the original words. Compare your version with the original.

____

____

____

____

____

C. Each of the two words in parentheses has almost the same meaning. In each sentence, write the word that is the better choice in the blank.

1. There were six ______________________ in Emma's family. (girls, lasses)
2. Their father was a ______________________. (rich man, moneybags)
3. Emma wrote ______________________. (rhymes, poetry)
4. She was very ______________________. (sensitive, thin-skinned)
5. The ______________________ arrived. (statue, figurine)
6. It was a ______________________ from France. (donation, gift)
7. Many ______________________ tried to raise money. (folks, people)

Footprints in Devonshire

On the night of February 8, 1885, snow fell on Devonshire, England. It began a little before 8 P.M. and stopped at midnight.

The next morning at 6 A.M., Henry Pilk, a baker, left his house. Soon he saw a path of footprints across his enclosed yard. Each print was U-shaped as if it had been made by a pony.

Henry frowned. The hoofprints were all in a line, one in front of the other. Neither people nor animals walked in this fashion.

Soon other people were out looking at the strange prints in the snow. In places, the hoofprints led to a wall as high as ten feet. Then they started again on the other side. All of the prints were four inches long. They were spaced about eight inches apart.

The trails led to every house in town, though they never doubled back. Prints were found in Topsham and in Totnes, 99 miles apart. Yet only six hours had elapsed from the time the snow ended until Pilk saw them. Prints were tracked to the Exe River at a point where it was about two miles wide. They continued on the other side of the river. Everywhere the prints were the same. Nowhere was there a sign that the creature rested.

Much snow fell during the next few days. Never did the tracks reappear. People carried weapons and avoided lonely places.

The *London Times* and other newspapers reported the story of the hoofprints. Experts claimed the prints came from giant rats, birds, rabbits, and kangaroos. But no one ever solved the mystery.

A. *Synonyms* are words that have the same meaning or almost the same meaning. Write a synonym for each of the underlined words below. Write the synonym above the words they replace.

1. Neither people nor animals walked in this <u>fashion</u>.

2. Many people <u>looked at</u> the strange prints in the snow.

3. Only six hours had <u>elapsed</u> from the time the snow ended until they were seen.

4. The tracks did not <u>reappear</u>.

5. Newspapers <u>reprinted</u> the story throughout the country.

6. The footprints crossed the enclosed yard.

7. The snow fell gently during the night.

8. Prints were tracked to the Exe River.

9. No one could explain where the tracks came from.

10. The tracks frightened many people.

B. The footprints look like they were made by a one-legged horse! This is impossible. It is possible to know the names of different kinds of horses—the four-legged kind. Use the clues to see how many you know. Some letters are given to help you.

filly	mare	mustang
pony	colt	thoroughbred
stallion	shetland	pinto

1. --- --- r --- – a mature, female horse
2. --- --- --- --- y – a young, female horse
3. --- --- --- t – a young, male horse
4. --- --- --- y – a young horse, male or female
5. m --- --- --- --- --- g – a small, wild horse found in the Southwest
6. t --- --- --- --- --- --- --- --- --- --- d – purebred, pedigreed horse
7. --- --- --- l --- --- --- n – a mature male horse
8. --- --- --- --- o – a favorite Indian pony
9. s --- --- t --- --- --- d – a tiny pony

C. The Devonshire footprints puzzled everyone. These scrambled synonyms puzzled them, too. See if you can unscramble the words in Column B and match them with their clues in Column A. The first one is done for you.

	Column A	Column B	
______	1. announce	a. osheu	house
______	2. dawn	b. ratts	______
______	3. small horse	c. dne	______
______	4. human beings	d. herryweeve	______
______	5. begin	e. nypo	______
a	6. home	f. ewf	______
______	7. stop	g. risenus	______
______	8. all over	h. dcelaer	______
______	9. several	i. leeppo	______

D. Many words have more than one synonym. The words below are all synonyms for the underlined words. Put each synonym in the correct column.

uncommon	alien	private	small	miniature
short	odd	secluded	deserted	mysterious
remote	brief	tiny	slight	unfrequented
solitary	unusual	incredible		

little	strange	lonely
______	______	______
______	______	______
______	______	______
______	______	______
______	______	______
______	______	______

The Smith Is a Lady

Ada Gates is said to be the only woman in the United States with a union card for horseshoeing. This unique blacksmith lives in Southern California. She works at the racetrack replacing the shoes of racehorses. She shoes an average of seven horses a day. That amounts to changing over 160 shoes each week!

Ada's day begins at 6 A.M. She prepares her gear and gets to the track by 8 A.M. She works straight through until 4 P.M., except for a few minutes for lunch. She is home again by 6 P.M., bone weary.

A groom holds her "clients" while she works, but often the horse is frightened. "You have to use all your strength to hold the animals while you're fitting the shoes. It puts a tremendous strain on your back," she says.

She wears only a leather apron over her clothes. Ada has suffered her share of bruises in her years as a licensed blacksmith. "Once I was kicked in the head and knocked out," she said.

Horses' shoes are made of steel and aluminum and bought from a supply house. Most are open shoes. Occasionally a horse needs a bar shoe, which is closed all the way around. These shoes are used for horses with leg problems.

A blacksmith such as Ada Gates first prepares the hoof. Then the shoe is welded and shaped. She is very careful in her work.

"The fit of a shoe is as crucial to a racehorse's running as a jockey," Ada points out.

A. Match the words with their meanings. Write the correct letter in the blank.

---------- 1. groom — a. once in a while

---------- 2. blacksmith — b. a person hired to take care of a horse

---------- 3. occasionally — c. of greatest importance

---------- 4. crucial — d. great

---------- 5. gear — e. a person who shoes horses

---------- 6. tremendous — f. equipment

B. ***Antonyms*** **are words that have opposite or nearly opposite meanings. Make the following statements correct by replacing the underlined words with antonyms. Write the antonyms above the words they replace.**

1. Gates goes to bed early.

2. She puts away her gear every morning.

3. After work, she is very energetic.

4. She seldom needs a groom to help her.

5. The horses she works on are fearless.

6. Weakness is a requirement for her job.

C. The underlined words in the sentences below are followed by two words in parentheses. One of these words is an antonym of the underlined word. The other word is its synonym. Cross out the synonym.

1. A horseshoe is said to bring good luck. (excellent, terrible)
2. Many people think this a false belief. (incorrect, true)
3. They think any lucky charm is silly. (childish, sensible)
4. Other people think lucky charms can't hurt. (believe, disbelieve)
5. Many are sure that the charms do bring luck. (doubtful, certain)
6. They tell true stories of their experiences. (fictional, actual)
7. One very poor woman found $100. (penniless, wealthy)
8. One very sad and lonely girl made a good friend. (cheerful, unhappy)
9. A shy boy became a movie star. (bashful, out-going)
10. Maybe a lucky charm is a good thing to have! (possibly, definitely)

A Dazzling Land

In Sri Lanka you must get permission if you want to dig in your backyard! Sri Lanka is an island. It lies in the Indian Ocean southeast of India. It was formerly called Ceylon. The island is rich with gemstones. The government wants to record and tax any gems that are found.

True stories of "finds" on Sri Lanka make it sound like a fairyland. One person found a 2,967 carat ruby and a huge blue sapphire. Another person found a star sapphire. After this stone was cut and polished, it became the Star of Sri Lanka. It is the world's third largest star sapphire.

In 1976, a very poor farmer in the district of Patnapura gave up his small plot of land. He went searching for gemstones. In one season he found a fortune in rough stones. They were worth over $200,000. The average yearly income in Sri Lanka is $200. That means he made 1000 times as much as ordinary workers receive.

For a long time smuggling was very common. Stones were constantly being sent out of the country. They were hidden in every kind of object, even corpses.

Since 1973, the government has had very strict regulations. Now a license is needed to deal in gems. Open auctions must be held. These new laws have stopped some smuggling, but not all. Some people still work in remote places at night by lantern light. Others meet and trade stones secretly. Many find that the precious stones bring only a long jail term.

Experts say that there are many more gems still waiting to be found on the island. Sri Lanka is truly a treasure hunter's paradise.

A. *Homonyms* are words that sound alike but have different meanings. For example, *carat* and *carrot* are homonyms. In each of the sentences below, fill in the blank with the homonym of the underlined word.

1. He won thousands of dollars in just ______________ season.
2. The farmer had read that the ruby is a ______________ stone.
3. One man flew to Sri Lanka and found ______________ gems.
4. He saw the ________________ glow of a pearl in his pail.
5. The site where the gems were found is in ____________________.
6. The farmer did not ________________ that no gems had been found there recently.

B. Below are pairs of homonyms. Choose the correct word to complete each sentence. Write it in the blank.

not	knot	1. The sailor could easily tie a ------------------ that could be untied quickly.
poll	pole	2. The governor said that a ------------------ had been taken to see what voters thought about the issue.
lean	lien	3. My mother tells me at almost every meal not to ------------------ on the table.
feat	feet	4. The broadjumper sailed through the air and landed ten ------------------ from the take-off board.
meat	meet	5. The track ------------------ ended at 5 P.M., as scheduled.
peek	peak	6. The climbers stopped to rest only when they reached the ------------------ of the mountain.
lien	lean	7. I like corned beef only if it is ------------------.
way	weigh	8. The grocer could not -------------------- the vegetables because the scale was broken.

C. Match each word with its synonym. Write the correct letter in the blank.

--------- 1. formerly	a. rules
--------- 2. true	b. average
--------- 3. huge	c. exchange
--------- 4. common	d. previously
--------- 5. sent out	e. permit
--------- 6. regulations	f. actual
--------- 7. license	g. immense
--------- 8. trade	h. exported

Women Auctioneers

"When you become an auctioneer, you first spend a lot of time talking to the wall," says Pamela Brown. "But all the practice in the world only goes so far. You've got to get up there and fly. Then you know you'll be fine."

Pam should know. She has just started "flying" as an auctioneer. She is one of a growing number of women who are entering this line of work. Many already are quite successful. Three of New York City's major auction galleries are conducted by women. They are entering a field that used to be all male.

Pam and her female co-workers have two things in common. They love their work, and they dislike being called women auctioneers.

Laura Kelly is the senior woman in the field in New York. She is very good at what she does. She has pride in her work. She says, "This business of being a woman auctioneer, ugh. I'm not a woman auctioneer. I'm an auctioneer."

Language often gives people the idea that only men or women do certain jobs. Soon we begin to think in terms of men-jobs and women-jobs. This use of language is sexist. Rewrite the following sentences to remove any sexism. The first is done for you.

1. Pam Brown is a woman auctioneer.

   Pam Brown is an auctioneer.

2. The woman doctor walked into the operating room.

   ____

3. The policeman opened the door of the police car and got in.

   ____

4. The workmen carried the bricks to the building site.

   ____

5. Women like to buy groceries in a store that gives good value and high quality.

   ____

   ____

Power to Bounty Island

In 1974, an aerospace engineer made an interesting bet. The bet had nothing to do with space rockets. It did involve fuel. He bet that he could provide energy for a home more cheaply than had ever been done before. He asked a physics teacher to help him. The teacher agreed. In addition, the teacher made it a project for his students.

Interest grew. Radio shows talked it up. Soon many people were talking about the energy project. News of it even spread to Pitcairn Island in the Pacific. There Tom Christian heard about it. Tom is a descendent of Fletcher Christian, the mutineer made famous in *Mutiny of the Bounty*. Tom was paying $4.00 a gallon for fuel. A low-cost solar generator was just what he needed. He gave his support to the project.

The class got to work. They used only old parts to build the solar unit. The frame for the unit was a butcher's counter. Reflectors were placed on top of this frame. It took 240 square mirrors to collect sunlight. Part of a Model T Ford was added to the frame. Oil-well casings and wire were used. An old motorcycle engine gave them power.

Then all they needed was sunlight. The mirrors would collect the light and focus the beams on boilers. The boilers, filled with water, would produce steam. The steam would run the engine. The engine would then power the generator. The result would be electricity—if all went well.

All did go well. They were able to produce electricity. Their simple machine worked. It was assembled near the end of 1980 in Pitcairn Island. Today it runs every fan and freezer on the island. Plus, it has power to spare. All the unit needs is the sun. And the bounty of Pitcairn Island is its long days of warm sunlight. The engineer won his bet. He proved that the sun, with the help of hard-working students can provide us all with cheap, clean energy that will never run out.

A. From each pair of homonyms below, choose the appropriate word to best complete the following sentences. Write it in the blank.

son sun — 1. The source of energy for the earth is the ______________.

days daze — 2. The boys sat in a ________________ after the car accident.

four for — 3. It was ________________ o'clock in the morning when we got home.

need knead	4.	Father always helps --------------------- the bread when we bake on Saturdays.
here hear	5.	The man told the operator that he couldn't ------------------ well.

B. Match the following types of energy with their appropriate definitions. Write the correct letter in the blank.

---------- 1. oil	a. energy from the sun caught in cells on panels; in the future could be cheap and limitless
---------- 2. coal	b. "earth heat"—sometimes used in the form of hot springs or dry steam
---------- 3. natural gas	c. force of water caught by dams and converted into electricity
---------- 4. wood	d. "black gold"—largest source of energy used today
---------- 5. nuclear	e. grains distilled into alcohol; could be used in automobiles
---------- 6. solar	f. popular for use in fireplaces
---------- 7. wind	g. third largest source of energy, these black rocks are mined
---------- 8. agricultural products	h. uranium based; produced in large reactors
---------- 9. geothermal	i. second largest source of energy; neither liquid or solid, it is drilled from far beneath the ground
----------10. hydroelectric	j. windmills and larger turbines are used to turn this force into usable power

C. Complete the "powerful" puzzle below. The first word is written in the puzzle.

Across

1. assignments; jobs
6. name of a ship; something freely given; riches
12. to gamble
23. homonym of 21 Down
27. to put together
36. synonym of 12 across
48. rebellion on a ship
54. something that throws back light
67. synonym of 48 across
79. synonym of 1 across
87. either/—
90. opposite of "yes"
101. to bring together
109. what the eyes do
114. to understand
122. to aid

Down

1. synonym of 6 across
6. synonym of 27 across
10. also
13. oil and gas are types of it
18. ocean
21. stitch
23. source of solar energy
47. child, grandchild, great-grandchild, etc., of a common ancestor
48. synonym of 54 across
61. synonym of 47 down
70. homonym of 87 across
73. homonym of 23 down
78. synonym of 101 across
99. synonym of 122 across
103. homonym of 10 down

1 T	2 A	3 S	4 K	5 S		6	7	8	9	10	11			12	13	14
15						16				17		18			19	
20			21			22			23	24		25			26	
27	28	29	30	31	32	33	34		35		36	37	38	39	40	
41			42			43			44						45	
46				47						48	49	50	51	52	53	
54	55	56	57	58	59	60	61	62		63						
64				65			66			67	68	69	70	71	72	
		73		74			75			76			77			78
79	80	81	82	83	84	85	86			87	88		89		90	91
		92		93			94			95						96
				97			98					99				100
101	102	103	104	105	106		107					108		109	110	111
		112		113		114	115	116	117			118				119
				120			121			122	123	124	125	126	127	128

But She's So Lovable

Sally is a yellowish tan Labrador retriever with the face of an angel and a spirit to match. She offers unlimited love and total loyalty. Most of the time she is the perfect pet.

Sally wags her tail furiously if you even look her way. A happy dog's tail is a joy to see. It is all motion. The motion is free, fast, and, it would seem, uncontrollable. Things tend to get swiped out of place. Often the things never return to their original places but find new homes in the garbage can.

Sally loves to be with you. Absence seems to make her heart grow even fonder. When you come back into a room after just a short time away, you receive a royal welcome. You are apt to get a big, slobbery kiss or Sally's muddy paws hugging your chest or shoulders.

You don't need to worry about what she'll eat. The answer is "anything." If she can't eat your newest slippers, she'll at least have them well-chewed for you.

When she does go on a chewing binge, almost nothing is neglected. She's handled fence posts—wood or metal—picnic tables, garden hoses, plastic toys, shovel handles, and more.

After her meals, she is content. She likes to just lie back and think about life while cleaning her teeth. She knows you want to do the same. There is no need to bother you for a toothpick. She makes her own from end tables, fancy chairs, or whatever is handy. She is a very easy to please, neat dog.

A. In each of the pairs below, identify whether the pairs are synonyms, antonyms, or homonyms. Write the correct word in the blank.

1. unlimited—endless ______________________
2. uncontrollable—obedient ______________________
3. apt—likely ______________________
4. write—right ______________________
5. absence—presence ______________________
6. loyalty—devotion ______________________
7. perfect—flawed ______________________
8. frequently—seldom ______________________
9. mite—might ______________________
10. neglected—forgotten ______________________

B. This is a vocabulary brainstorm. You are to think of words that relate to wood. A sample word in each group is given to get you started.

Words with "wood" in them	Words of things made of wood	Words of things involving wood
woodwork	table	forest
__________	__________	__________
__________	__________	__________
__________	__________	__________
__________	__________	__________
__________	__________	__________
__________	__________	__________
__________	__________	__________
__________	__________	__________

Tumblelogs

Just like the cowboy and the campfire, the tumbleweed was a part of the Old West. Today it is simply a nuisance, an unwanted weed. But science may revive interest in the tumbleweed. There is a new invention called "the tumblelog." If it is successful, it may be a new source of fuel.

U.S. Department of Energy

Tumblelogs are made by grinding tumbleweeds into sawdust. Then a log machine compresses the sawdust and shapes it into a log. This log is like the "chemical logs" on the market, but is in some ways better. The price of both will

U.S. Department of Energy

Marjorie and Aden Mienel at the University of Arizona in Tucson have converted tumbleweeds into "tumblelogs." Their project is partially funded by the U.S. Department of Energy.

be about the same. The tumblelog will be able to burn longer. The chemical log can damage wood stoves. The tumblelog will be safe in both fireplaces and wood stoves.

Other uses for the ground-up tumbleweed are also being studied. In research labs, tumbleweed dust is being mixed with coal dust. The mixture may make a fuel that can be used instead of oil. A liquid form could one day replace gasoline.

No one knows if a major new source for fuel has been found. Much more testing must be done. The tumbleweed should be accepted as an effective fuel. It could solve many energy problems. It could also solve some farming problems. Desert land could be changed into rich farms. Tumbleweed could be sown and tended. One acre of land could yield enough tumbleweed to make more than 5000 logs. At fifty cents a log, a farmer could make thousands of dollars. At these prices, "tumblin' tumbleweed" may be again a favorite sight in the West.

A. Following is a list of words. In one column write a synonym for each word. In the other column write an antonym.

	Synonym	Word	Antonym
1.	------------------------------	part	------------------------------
2.	------------------------------	unwanted	------------------------------
3.	------------------------------	revive	------------------------------
4.	------------------------------	new	------------------------------
5.	------------------------------	safe	------------------------------
6.	------------------------------	major	
7.	------------------------------	effective	------------------------------
8.	------------------------------	desert	------------------------------
9.	------------------------------	yield	------------------------------
10.	------------------------------	tend	------------------------------

B. Cross out the word which doesn't match the meaning of the two other words.

1. flammable inflammable non-flammable
2. artificial phoney actual

3. damage repair break
4. sell give grant
5. expand compress reduce
6. deregulate control influence
7. worthless valuable helpful
8. change preserve transform
9. disliked popular accepted

C. Replace the underlined words with a synonym. Write the synonym above the word you replace.

1. Today tumbleweed is a nuisance.
2. It may be a new source of fuel.
3. To make a tumblelog, first grind up tumbleweeds.
4. The price of both logs will be about the same.
5. It could solve many energy problems.

D. Think of some words used in talking about the Old West. Try to think of some of the good things in the West in pioneer times as well as some of the bad aspects. Here are some to start you off.

1. old doggies ____________ 2. campfires ____________
3. tumblin' tumbleweed ____________ 4. ____________
5. ____________ 6. ____________
7. ____________ 8. ____________
9. ____________ 10. ____________

Turtles Can Live Over Two Hundred Years

The turtle may be one of the slowest animals. It is also one of the longest living creatures. Turtles were on the earth long before we were. They seem to have learned something about survival. Giant tortoises have been known to live over 200 years. Some may have even lived 300 years.

Why does the hard-shelled creature live so long? Because it takes life easy!

A turtle eats slowly, grows slowly, moves slowly, and even breathes at a very slow rate. It takes more than a year for the shell to harden. Some turtle eggs take as long as a year to hatch.

During the winter months, the turtle hibernates. Its body functions slow down at this time. It moves so slowly that it seems to be hardly alive. It burrows down into the mud at the bottom of an ocean, lake, river, or pond. This creature is cold-blooded. It has the same temperature as the mud. The mud is just warm enough to keep it from freezing.

Turtles can be found on land and in fresh and salt water. Turtles vary greatly in size. The Galapagos, a land tortoise, can weigh up to 500 pounds. The average leatherneck—the largest sea variety—often weighs about 1,000 pounds!

Donald E. Trinko/Tom Stack & Associates

A. Match the following words with their synonyms. Write the correct letter in the blank.

----------	1. hibernates	a. barely
----------	2. since	b. works
----------	3. functions	c. differ
----------	4. hardly	d. sleeps
----------	5. burrows	e. typical
----------	6. vary	f. type
----------	7. variety	g. because
----------	8. average	h. digs

B. Write an antonym for each word below.

1. slowly ______________
2. survival ______________
3. harden ______________
4. bottom ______________
5. barely ______________
6. body ______________
7. same ______________
8. warm ______________
9. giant ______________
10. freezing ______________

C. All of the words below relate in some way to being old. Use the correct word in each sentence below. (You may use a dictionary if your teacher permits). Words can be used more than once.

ancient	elderly	pensioner
antiques	geriatrics	octogenarians

Dr. Sheila Graham is my grandmother's doctor. She is a specialist in ______________. My grandmother likes to go to Dr. Graham. There are many medical tools on display in Dr. Graham's office. Most of Dr. Graham's ______________ patients enjoy seeing these tools from the past. Most of the tools are about 100 years old. This makes them ______________, but they certainly aren't ______________.

Dr. Graham comes from Britain. Her father still lives there. He's retired and therefore is known as a ______________. There are many ______________, or people in their eighties. Mr. Graham lives in an ______________ castle, full of very old furniture and other ______________. Dr. Graham says you'd hardly know her father was ______________ if you saw him. He looks more like age 40 than age 85.

USING CONTEXT CLUES

Animal Language

What do a canary and a mule have in common? Dr. Eugene Morton has come up with a surprising answer. His studies show that all animals, including humans, have common language patterns. This does not mean that a mule can sing. Nor does it mean that a canary can tell a joke. It does mean that all animals get their ideas across to each other in a similar way.

Stated simply, Morton says there are three basic tones in animal language. A low, harsh sound or growl shows anger. A high sound or whine is used for friendly meetings. An in-between sound, a kind of bark, shows uncertainty or a need for attention.

Morton used a spectrograph in his work. This instrument changes sounds into pictures. The picture of growls is always the same. Growls show up as thick, heavy bands at the lower end of the scale. It makes no difference who does the growling. A pig's growl looks the same as a pelican's growl. The whine shows up as a thin line higher up on the scale. The bark or grunt is V-shaped on the spectrograph.

Voice Identification, Inc.

Sound Spectrograph

The size of the animal does not affect the loudness of a sound. Many small animals have learned to be as noisy as possible. By sounding loud, they prevent attacks by larger animals. In the same way, a huge lion with its mate or cubs purrs as softly as a pet kitten.

The same system is used by humans. Loud cries or yells are used when fighting. Soft tones are used when trying to win someone's favor. Ordinary tones are used in giving information. If read aloud, this article would be one long series of barks!

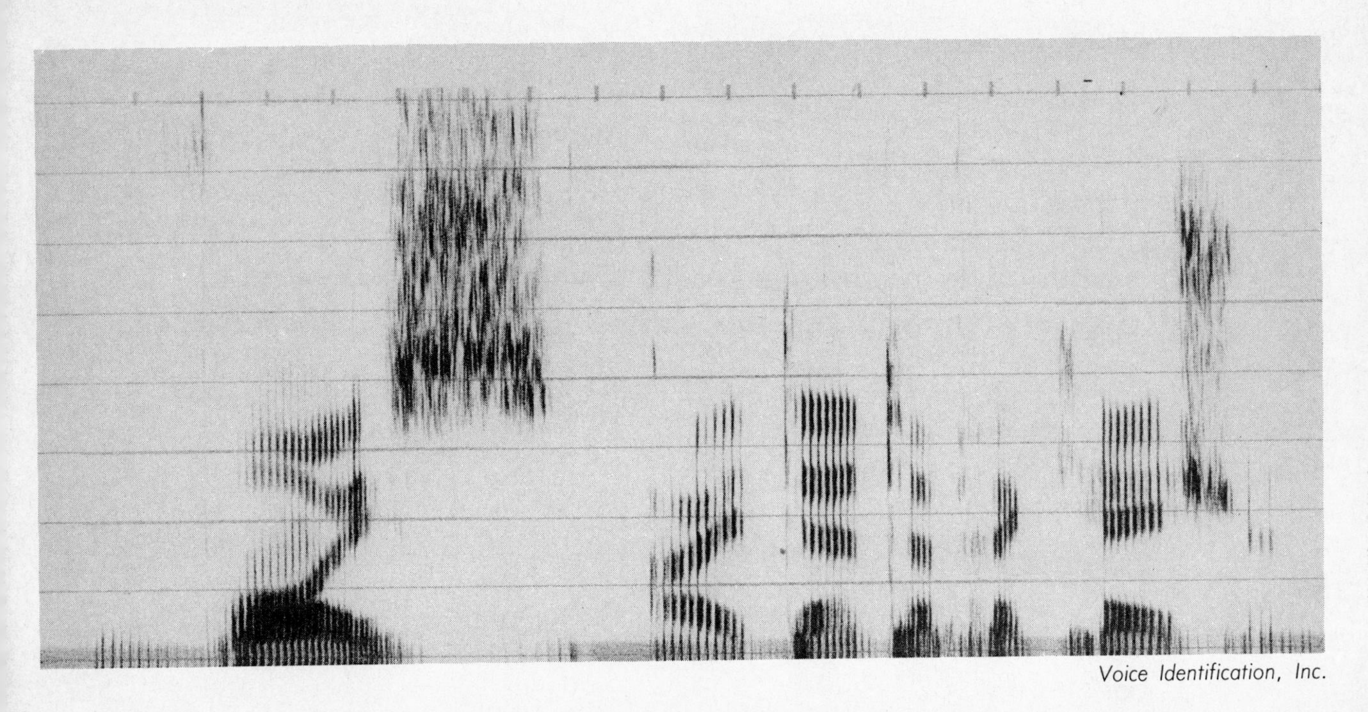

Voice Identification, Inc.

This printout depicts a male voice saying the phrase "voice identification."

A. The way a word is used in a sentence often gives clues to its meaning. Use these context clues to find the meaning of the underlined word. Circle the letter of the correct meaning.

1. Animals have language patterns. They get their ideas across to each other in a similar way.
   - a. regular ways of doing something
   - b. varied sounds
   - c. voice boxes

2. A low, harsh sound or growl shows anger.
   - a. pleasing to the ear
   - b. dangerous
   - c. unpleasantly sharp or rough

3. By sounding loud, small animals <u>prevent</u> attacks by larger animals.
   a. invite
   b. keep from happening
   c. fight valiantly

4. Loud cries are used when fighting. Soft <u>tones</u> are used when trying to win someone's favor.
   a. colors
   b. sounds
   c. foods

B. Each sentence is missing a word. Circle the letter of the word that best completes the sentence.

1. The ---------- changes sounds into a picture.
   a. telegraph
   b. radarscope
   c. sonograph

2. A dog's ---------- shows up at the lower end of the scale.
   a. bark
   b. growl
   c. whine

3. Smaller animals ---------- attacks by being noisy.
   a. cause
   b. discourage
   c. fight off

4. Animals often make ---------- sounds when in danger of attack.
   a. soft
   b. unpleasant
   c. frightened

5. Animals ---------- ideas through sounds according to Eugene Morton.
   a. speak
   b. share
   c. have

C. Indicate whether the following pairs are synonyms, antonyms, or homonyms. Write the correct word in the blank.

1. suggests—demands --
2. ideas—thoughts --
3. read—red --
4. similar—different --
5. uncertainty—confidence --
6. scale—register --
7. favor—approval --
8. information—facts --

D. Some words can have more than one meaning. The words below have more than one meaning. From the context, decide which word belongs in each blank. Write the correct word in each blank.

studies common state attention

1. Before a test, John always ------------------------------ hard.
2. For this special dinner, she didn't want to serve any ------------------------------ foods.
3. The largest ------------------------------ in the United States is Alaska.
4. The soldiers stood at ------------------------------ when the flag was raised.
5. The nasty wound needs a doctor's ------------------------------.
6. The twins found out that they had many things in ------------------------------.
7. The research lab released the latest ------------------------------ on cancer.
8. The reports ------------------------------ that smoking is dangerous.

Hawaii's Big Fish Event

Most of us enjoy fishing. It is fun to sit under a tree with a pole and wait for a fish to bite. For most of us, fishing is a very relaxing sport. For big-game anglers, fishing means something very different. These people go after fish many times their own size. For them, fishing is a fast-paced, exciting sport. They match their skill against the tremendous weight and strength of the fish. Many make this sport even more exciting. They enter competitions.

One of big-game fishing's most challenging event is not very well-known. It is the Hawaiian Islands' Billfish Tournament. It is held each year on the big island of Hawaii. The best of the big-game anglers all take part. They gather here in July. The event lasts for two months.

The waters off Hawaii are quiet and warm. One of the world's largest concentrations of immense fish are found here. Participants fish for marlin, yellow fish, tuna, sailfish, and spearfish. They may also catch jack crevalle, dophin-fish, and wahoo. The challenge is incredible.

Each day spectators crowd the dock to watch the weigh-ins. For Hawaiians and those in the event, it is like the World Series and the Super Bowl.

Hawaii Visitors Bureau

A. Use context clues to help you understand the meaning of the underlined words in the story. Choose the correct meaning for each word. Circle the letter of that choice.

1. relaxing
   a. thrilling
   b. restful
   c. boring

2. tremendous
   a. enormous
   b. wonderful
   c. fearful

3. tournament

a. parade

b. carnival

c. contest

4. participants

a. those who take part

b. those who watch

c. those who assist

B. Match these words with their definitions as used in the story. Write the correct letter in the blank.

---------- 1. event

---------- 2. concentration

---------- 3. immense

---------- 4. competition

---------- 5. spectators

---------- 6. challenging

a. happening

b. contest

c. large group

d. people who watch an event

e. difficult

f. huge, very big

C. The following words have more than one meaning. From the context, decide which word belongs in each blank. Write the correct word in each blank.

part last known like

1. My brother needed one ------------------------ to repair a bicycle.
2. The lost campers were forced to eat the ------------------------ candy bar.
3. I have ------------------------ my neighbors all my life.
4. In the summer, I ------------------------ to eat fresh fish.
5. To me, my dog is ------------------------ Benji and Lassie rolled into one.
6. The class seemed to ------------------------ forever.
7. Everyone was invited to take ------------------------ in the school play.
8. The president is ------------------------ throughout the world.

The Founder of the WASPs

Jacqueline Cochran was not only a great aviator, she was a model for all women.

Cochran began flying when she was quite young. She soon became a favorite of newspaper writers. They felt that she was brave and adventurous.

She was the first woman to enter the Bendix Air Races. In 1937 she came in third. The next year she won the Bendix Trophy.

In 1941 Cochran joined the war effort. She was the first woman to fly a bomber over the Atlantic. She was a flight captain in the British Transport Auxiliary. She trained a group of women for air transport service. They flew bombers to war zones.

Jacqueline Cochran had many "firsts." Of all her achievements, she will mostly be remembered for one. She founded the Womens' Airforce Service Pilots, the WASPs. She saw the need for this unit. She made President Franklin Delano Roosevelt see the need also. Early in World War II she persuaded him to allow the unit to be formed.

Cochran organized and trained the group. Their duties were dangerous. They had to ferry bombers and fighter

U.S. Air Force

Jacqueline Cochran as director of women pilots is reviewing a squadron.

U.S. Air Force

planes to combat forces. There the planes were used by male air force pilots.

In 1945, Cochran scored another first. She was awarded the Distinguished Service Medal. She was the first woman civilian ever to receive it. Three years later she received a commission. She became a lieutenant colonel in the Air Force Reserves.

The end of World War II did not mean the end of flying for Cochran. She continued to try for new speed and long distance records. In 1963 she flew a plane at twice the speed of sound.

Women now fly for major airlines in many parts of the world. In large part, they have the chance because of Jacqueline Cochran.

A. Use the words underlined in the above selection to fill in the blanks before each definition.

1. ______________________ liking excitement and adventure
2. ______________________ rank in the military forces
3. ______________________ jobs one must do
4. ______________________ best liked
5. ______________________ to transport from one place to another on a regular basis
6. ______________________ an airplane pilot
7. ______________________ convinced
8. ______________________ an assisting group

B. Use context clues to help you choose the best meaning for each underlined word. Circle the letter of the best meaning.

1. Jacqueline Cochran was a model for women. Other women want to follow in her footsteps.
   a. a person who helps others
   b. a person who inspires others
   c. a person who fights for others

2. In the Bendix Air Races, she won the Bendix Trophy. It now sits proudly on her desk.
   a. cash prize
   b. medal
   c. statue

3. They flew bombers to war zones. These places were dangerous.
   a. outskirts of a place
   b. an area of land
   c. battles

4. She will be remembered for her achievements. She did a great deal.
   a. work successfully done
   b. military honors
   c. ability

5. She was the first woman civilian to receive a military medal.
   a. a person in the military
   b. a non-commissioned officer
   c. a non-military person

C. Choose the word that best completes each sentence. Circle the correct letter.

1. Mary enjoyed flying. She hoped one day to be a(n) ----------.
   a. model
   b. colonel
   c. aviatrix

2. The wounded man had to make a(n) --------- to save himself before the night came on.
   a. trial
   b. effort
   c. plea

3. The entire seventh grade will form one --------- in the city parade.
   a. unit
   b. area
   c. auxiliary

4. The dog was --------- a medal for the brave rescue of its master.
   a. commissioned
   b. awarded
   c. fetched

D. Find the two pairs of synonyms, the two pairs of antonyms, and the two pairs of homonyms in the columns below. Write the pairs in the blanks.

won	two
first	slowly
allow	too
combat	last
quickly	one
permit	battle

1. synonyms ------------------------------------ ------------------------------------
2. synonyms ------------------------------------ ------------------------------------
3. antonyms ------------------------------------ ------------------------------------
4. antonyms ------------------------------------ ------------------------------------
5. homonyms ------------------------------------ ------------------------------------
6. homonyms ------------------------------------ ------------------------------------

A Master of Sophisticated Terror

His movies invite the viewer to scream. Until his death in 1980, he was the master of terror. He hatched dark plots out of our secret fears. All the things that go bump in the night lurked around him. He was Alfred Hitchcock, an inventive man known for his wit.

Wide World Photos

Hitchcock began his career with the silent movies. He was one of the first to see the possibilities of using sound. In 1929, he made Britain's first talkie. This was the film *Blackmail*. He used the new medium with skill. Sound gave him a new way to create horror. In this first film, the word *knife* was repeated over and over. The effect was eerie.

Hitch, as he was usually known, was famous for his film theory. He felt that preparation was everything. The filming was a bore. The real creative work had by that time been completed. Few directors agreed with him. They felt free to rewrite scripts to meet the needs of the film. Hitch did not. He rarely changed a finished script. His scripts were very precise. They often included sketches of scenes as he wanted them to look. He was true to his theory during his life.

One of Hitchcock's early films deals with Jack the Ripper. It begins with a close-up of a man's hand. The hand slips along a circular banister. The camera follows it as it moves down four long flights of stairs and out into the darkness. The next shot is a newspaper headline. It reports another Ripper murder.

A. For each word below write a definition. Refer to the selection to see how each word was used. The paragraph the word appears in is given to help you.

1. hatched (paragraph 1) --
2. lurked (paragraph 1) --
3. talkie (paragraph 2) --
4. eerie (paragraph 2) --

B. Circle the letter of the best answer to the following questions.

1. What do the words *dark plots* in paragraph 1 mean?
   a. unlighted sections of land
   b. evil plans
   c. scary stories

2. What did Hitchcock mean when he said "preparation was everything"?
   a. He didn't enjoy working with actors.
   b. Planning is very important in film-making.
   c. He didn't trust others to do his job for him.

3. The word *medium* has several meanings. Which meaning is used in paragraph 2?
   a. average
   b. a person who can contact the dead
   c. artistic technique

4. Why did only a few directors agree with Hitch's film theory?
   a. It was something new.
   b. It upset people's morality.
   c. People had different opinions about it.

C. The underlined words in the paragraph below all have synonyms in the Hitchcock story. Replace each underlined word with one of the synonyms or use one of your own choosing. Write your word above the one you replace.

The night was <u>black</u>. He could see nothing. He knew the enemy was out there. It <u>hid</u> behind every tree. He was afraid, but he realized that he had to keep his <u>fear</u> under control. He lit a match. Then he saw it. Its shape was not very <u>exact</u>, but it was there. The clock struck mid-night. A <u>round</u> shape rose from a nearby garden where it had been unnoticed, mixed with the flowers. Its laughing face chased him as he ran.

He was never seen again.

D. Use context clues to choose the best definition of each of the underlined words. Circle the letter of the correct definition.

1. Hitchcock was an inventive man known for his wit. He brought about many changes in the film industry.
   a. humor
   b. cleverness
   c. ability to create horror
2. Hitchcock saw the possibilities of using sound. He saw what movies could be.
   a. things that could happen
   b. things that would happen
   c. things that would never happen
3. The creative work was completed before the actual filming. Hitch, an inventive man, enjoyed this type of work the most.
   a. difficult
   b. imaginative
   c. active
4. Hitch rarely changed a finished script. Other directors almost always did.
   a. frequently
   b. seldom
   c. never
5. Hitchcock's film theory was not followed by many directors. Few agreed with his beliefs.
   a. terms
   b. method
   c. rules

The Ad That Produced a Writer

In 1916 Samuel Dashiel Hammett was a young high school dropout. He happened to read an ad in a Baltimore newspaper. It sounded intriguing enough to answer.

He had already tried several jobs up to this time. He had been a freight clerk and a railroad laborer. He had worked on the docks as a stevedore. The ad promised a different kind of life. It was put into the newspaper by the Pinkerton Agency.

Hammett got the job. The job did change his life. He was hired to become a Pinkerton detective. His job was based in San Francisco. At this time, the city was "the most politically corrupt" in the United States.

Hammett stayed with the job for eight years. As a private eye, he saw his share of corruption. He worked on the Nicky Arnstein swindle case and the Fatty Arbuckle case. His first promotion came when he captured a thief who had stolen a ferris wheel.

Next Hammett turned to writing. At 21, this young author published *Red Harvest*. Then came *The Dain Case*, *The*

Culver Pictures

Dashiell Hammett (left) with actor George Raft (center) and director Frank Tuttle (right). This photograph was taken during the filming of Hammett's mystery, *The Glass Key*.

Maltese Falcon, *The Glass Key*, and *The Thin Man*. His fictional detective, Sam Spade, became a household name.

Hammett was a colorful person. He was very dashing and somewhat radical. He was very strong in his beliefs. Many times his beliefs and comments got him into trouble.

A. Match the words in the left column with their definitions as used in the story. Write the letter of the correct definition in the blank.

---------- 1. based	a. interesting
---------- 2. corrupt	b. extreme in one's views
---------- 3. dropout	c. located
---------- 4. radical	d. a person who loads ships
---------- 5. intriguing	e. a person who quits
---------- 6. stevedore	f. dishonest

B. There are many names people use to describe private detectives. Some of these terms are slang. They would not be appropriate in all situations. Circle the letter before the place where you would appropriately find each name used for private detectives.

1. Gum Shoe
   a. mystery story
   b. newspaper article
   c. police report
2. Private Eye
   a. TV news
   b. TV dramatic program
   c. speech by the president of the United States
3. Private Investigator
   a. court of law
   b. comic book mystery
   c. joke about a private detective

Yogi Berra: The Man of Words

Yogi Berra was one of the all-time baseball greats. Yet he was not an untouchable hero. He was very human. He had one habit that his fans really liked. This was Yogi's use of the English language. Many times he said things he really did not mean. The words would get mixed up. The results were often funny. Whenever he did this, he would break any tension that heroes seem to create. From that point on, it was just Yogi and friends. Everyone would join in the laughter.

National Baseball Hall of Fame and Museum, Inc.

Perhaps the best known example of Yogi's way with words was his use of "wrong mistake." Another mixed-up statement came in 1964. He was then manager of the New York Yankees. He delighted his fans with his answer to a reporter. The reporter asked him if he knew enough for the job. Yogi answered, "Sure. I've been playing for eighteen years. You can observe a lot just by watching."

Once his old cronies and neighbors had a "Yogi Berra Night." Thousands of fans filled Sportsman Park in St. Louis. There was a new car and many smaller gifts for Yogi. Then it was time for his speech. He grasped the microphone. He said, "I want to thank everybody for making this night necessary."

One of the funniest examples of Yogi's habit was embarrassing when it first happened. He had wanted to compliment a young woman. What he actually said, however, was an insult! It happened in Florida. The day was very hot. Yogi had just finished playing ball. He showered and dressed in white pants, shoes, and polo shirt. A female fan greeted him. "Hello, Yogi," she said. "You look mighty cool."

Yogi replied, "You don't look too hot yourself."

There are more of these Yogi Berra sayings. They continue to amuse and cheer up those who know this well-loved baseball star.

A. Rewrite Yogi's mixed-up statements to make sense.

1. "Sure, I've been playing for eighteen years. You can observe a lot just by watching."

   ---

2. "I want to thank everybody for making this night necessary."

   ---

3. "You don't look too hot yourself."

B. In each sentence, choose the best definition for the underlined word. Use context clues to help you. Circle the letter of the best definition.

1. He was not an <u>untouchable</u> hero. He was very human.
   a. emotional
   b. always perfect
   c. very frail

2. His funny words would break the <u>tension</u> that heroes create.
   a. image
   b. nervousness
   c. laughter

3. His <u>old cronies</u> and neighbors honored him.
   a. fans
   b. family
   c. friends

4. One of Yogi's funny statements was <u>embarrassing</u> when it first happened.
   a. humorous
   b. awkward
   c. scandalous

C. Choose the word that best completes each sentence. Circle the correct letter.

1. It was time for Yogi's speech. He grasped the ----------.
   a. manager
   b. microphone
   c. baseball bat
2. These funny examples are only some of Yogi's ----------.
   a. sayings
   b. gifts
   c. habits
3. Yogi's speech ---------- his fans.
   a. upset
   b. embarrassed
   c. amused

D. The following words have more than one meaning. Use context clues to correctly complete the sentences. Write the correct word in each blank.

point grasp break use

1. The dog actually learned to ------------------------ to things his master named.
2. The baby likes to ------------------------ fingers tightly in her hand.
3. If that vase is dropped, it will ------------------------.
4. Older students ------------------------ pens rather than pencils.
5. The ------------------------ of pain-killing drugs was recommended for the very sick person.
6. The complicated lesson was beyond the student's ------------------------.
7. After a certain ------------------------, the sleepy child stopped listening.
8. After so much hard work, the players took a ------------------------.

Reversed Identities

A. Complete the story. Fill in the blanks with appropriate words from the list on page 41.

On August 4, 1914, the British luxury liner *Carmania* was steaming back to Liverpool. It was nearing the end of another successful cruise. All had gone well. The 800 passengers on board were enjoying the ______________ cabins, the good food, and the calm sea air. They looked forward to three more days of ______________ good times. Then came the news. The *Carmania* was ______________ that war had been declared. It would be ______________ to a warship. The fun was over.

The ship docked in Liverpool on August 7. One week later, the *Carmania* was again at sea. There was one difference. It was now a fully equipped, armed cruiser. It had a new ______________ to make it look more like enemy ships. Its disguise would permit it to get close to its enemies. It could then destroy them easily.

On September 2, the *Carmania* arrived in the West Indies. It was loaded with coal and wartime ______________. Its destination was Trinidad. Its mission was to ______________ for enemy ships. It reached Trinidad in three days. One hour and a half later an enemy ship was sighted. There was only one problem. The vessel's name was *Carmania*, and it looked just like the British ship. The officers and the crew thought they were seeing ghosts.

The other vessel was really the *Cap Trafalgar*, a German liner. It had also been converted to a warship. The *Cap Trafalgar* had been ______________ to look like the *Carmania*. It had even had one funnel removed to look like the British ship. Its plan was to move among the enemy ships and catch them unaware. Then it would destroy them.

The plan failed. On September 14, the disguised *Cap Trafalgar* was attacked and sunk by the *Carmania*. The scene was unreal. One ship was sinking, and one ship watched. Both had the same name. Both looked ______________. By chance, each ship had been disguised as the other. With all the oceans of the world to sail on, they happened to arrive in the same spot.

search—to look for
converted—changed into
disguised—made to look different; camouflaged
funnel—a smokestack on a ship
notified—told
provisions—supplies
plush—rich, elegant
identical—exactly alike
carefree—without problems

B. Just as the *Cap Trafalgar* was disguised, see if you can disguise one word! Write synonyms for the following words. See how the word is used in the story for ideas. You will be saying the same thing with each word but "in disguise."

	ship	plush	good	unreal
1.	----------------------	----------------------	----------------------	----------------------
2.	----------------------	----------------------	----------------------	----------------------
3.	----------------------	----------------------	----------------------	----------------------

C. Circle the letter of the meaning that best describes the underlined word.

1. The *Carmania* was a luxury liner. Everyone was enjoying the cruise.
   a. very large
   b. built for comfort
   c. average
2. Its destination was Trinidad. It had work to do there.
   a. point of departure
   b. battle scene
   c. place where one is going

3. Its mission was to search and destroy enemy ships. Those were its orders.

   a. ability

   b. desire

   c. purpose

4. In a short while an enemy ship was sighted. The battle would soon begin.

   a. attacked

   b. spotted

   c. disguised

5. Before they were aware of any danger, it could destroy them.

   a. were told about

   b. admitted

   c. realized

D. Cross out the word in each group that is different from the rest.

1. passengers	travelers	spectators
2. notified	warned	told
3. declared	announced	denounced
4. guarantee	permit	allow
5. provisions	weapons	supplies
6. corpses	ghosts	phantoms
7. destroy	kill	create
8. removed	added	taken away
9. disguised	uncovered	concealed
10. failed	succeeded	triumphed

Glowing Moss

Certain caves in Central Europe startle visitors. The walls, ceilings, and floors all gleam with a green-gold curtain of light. The rocks appear to have a lighting system inside. The "lighting system" is not bright. It is soft and eerie. It comes from a feathery gray-green moss on the surfaces of the rocks.

This moss produces many strands. The strands branch out in all directions. On the end of each strand are lens-shaped cells. The cells contain grains of green-colored matter, or chlorophyll.

The light in the cave is generally dim. The lens of each cell works with the faintest sparks of light. The lens concentrates all light at the bottoms of the cells. These parts on which the light is concentrated are very specialized. They allow the plant to carry on the photosynthesis process. Some of the light is reflected outward from the cells. Because of the chlorophyll in the cell, the light has an eerie green-gold color.

A. Match each word in the left column with its meaning as used in the story. Write the correct letter in the blank.

---------- 1. startle	a. to shine
---------- 2. eerie	b. flash
---------- 3. spark	c. happens when green plants use sunlight to make food
---------- 4. concentrate	d. to make stronger
---------- 5. photosynthesis	e. dim
---------- 6. condensed	f. strange
---------- 7. faint	g. surprise
---------- 8. gleam	h. shortened or reduced

B. The following words have more than one meaning. Use context clues to correctly complete the sentences. Write the correct word in each blank.

faint certain branch plant

1. A cat can see even in very ---------------------------- light.

2. The expert was ________________ about his facts.

3. The search party was told to ________________ out in all directions.

4. A ________________ needs light and water to grow.

5. The large tire company was opening up a new ________________ in our city.

6. The girl was allergic to ________________ foods.

7. The choirboy thought he was going to ________________ in the hot, crowded church.

8. A new ________________ of the library is being built in my neighborhood.

C. Circle the letter of the best definition for each underlined word.

1. The moss produces many <u>strands</u>. The strands branch out in all directions.

   a. cells

   b. rope-like stems

   c. leaves

2. On the end of each strand are <u>lens-shaped</u> cells.

   a. curved

   b. very small

   c. square

3. The <u>specialized</u> parts are involved in photosynthesis. They do nothing else.

   a. valuable

   b. adapted for one use

   c. hard-working

4. The light in the cave is generally <u>dim</u>.

   a. bright

   b. pitch black

   c. somewhat dark

A Perfumed Tower

Complete the story. Fill in the blanks with the appropriate words from the list at the end of the story.

Marrakesh, Morocco, is a strange and lovely land. It has many ______________________________ places for tourists to visit. One trip to a ______________________________ will delight visitors. The Koutoubiya Tower is beautiful. It has a sweet ______________________________ as well.

The scent is real. The tall, ______________________________ structure is known for its fragrance. It has had this scent for more than seven centuries. Nor is it ______________________________. Other towers share this same fragrance. They were all built in the golden years of Moslem architecture.

In 1195, the Sultan Yakul defeated the King of Castile in Spain. The ______________________________ at the time was to reward Mohammed for the victory. Therefore, Yakul built the tower. When the ______________________________ was mixed for the building, 960 sacks of musk ______________________________ were added. From that year long ago, the fragrance has been a part of the tower. This is not too surprising. Musk is one of the most lasting of all fragrances.

The tower is 66 meters high. From the top, visitors get a marvelous view of Marrakesh. For six centuries, though, only blind priests were allowed to climb all the way up. In those early days, the tower's peak would offer a view of the harems—a sight ______________________________ to men.

aroma—a pleasant smell
custom—something people are expected to do
forbidden—something that is not permitted
minaret—a slender tower attached to a mosque (Islamic temple)
mortar—a building material made of sand, water, lime, and cement
unique—the only one
perfume—a liquid that gives off a pleasant odor
slender—slim, skinny
exotic—strange, foreign

Thunderstorms, Hurricanes, and Tornadoes

A great poet once said, "A rose by any other name would smell as sweet." Something similar may be said about storms. They are called by a number of different names. No matter what they are called, all are violent weather disturbances. All can kill. They destroy in different ways and in different places. All have the same basic characteristic. All have air currents that move rapidly from one place to another.

The most common storms are thunderstorms. About 45,000 of these occur every day. They are triggered by strong rising air currents. As the air rises, it is cooled. Heat is released. This heat provides the energy that can develop into a storm. Thunderstorms are full of crackling thunder and blazing light. Usually their fury is quickly spent. They can kill but usually do not. They are the least dangerous of the storms.

National Oceanic and Atmospheric Administration

Hurricane

National Oceanic and Atmospheric Administration

Thunderstorm

A storm more to be feared is the hurricane. In some parts of the world, these storms are known as typhoons or tropical cyclones. East Indian and China Sea storms are known by these names. Nearer to home, these same types of storms would be called hurricanes. In the United States, they affect two areas. Cities along the East Coast and those that border the Gulf of Mexico usually get the brunt of these storms. Both the hurricane and the typhoon are tropical storms.

These tropical storms can be very large. One of the largest storms affected an area of over 400 miles. Hurricane winds have been clocked at speeds of over 125 miles an hour. The center of the swirling winds is calm. This inner part is called the "eye" of the storm. The eye may be from 5 to 16 miles wide. It, too, can cause havoc. As it passes over an area, the winds reverse and strike from the opposite direction. Hurricanes are very dangerous, especially along coasts. Here the winds churn the sea. Storm waves and rain cause severe flooding.

Another violent storm is the tornado. Tornadoes have a much smaller storm area than hurricanes. Their path may be only a few miles long and a few hundred feet wide. In that area, however, they are just as severe. Almost everything in their path is destroyed. A tornado is a fast-moving, funnel-shaped cloud. It begins in a larger thunderstorm area. It forms when a downward draft comes from a rain cloud. This type of storm is most often found in the Midwest.

Wichita Falls Times

Tornado

A. Define these words from information in the story.

1. thunderstorm --

----

2. hurricane ---

----

3. tornado ---

B. Match each word with its antonym. Write the correct letter in the blank.

---------- 1. calm a. create

---------- 2. destroy b. frigid

---------- 3. tropical c. slow

---------- 4. common d. violent

---------- 5. rapid e. rare

C. Answer the questions from information in the story. Circle the letter of the correct answer.

1. What does this quote mean, "A rose by any other name would smell as sweet"?
   a. All flowers smell sweet.
   b. A name does not change what something is.
   c. The name of something that smells sweet is a rose.
2. What do all storms have in common?
   a. All have air that moves rapidly from one place to another.
   b. All are formed in the tropics.
   c. All storms have funnel clouds.
3. What is an air "current"?
   a. streams
   b. clouds
   c. movements
4. Why are some hurricanes called typhoons?
   a. Typhoons are more dangerous than hurricanes.
   b. Typhoons have winds of over 200 miles per hour.
   c. Typhoons are the names of hurricanes in the Far East.
5. How does a tornado differ from a thunderstorm?
   a. A tornado covers a larger area.
   b. A tornado is not as dangerous as a thunderstorm.
   c. A tornado can destroy anything in its path.

USING STRUCTURAL ANALYSIS

Pioneers of Flight

They lived in a magic time. They were among the first to reach out and seize the stars. They ventured into the sky and made it their own. The world watched in admiration. They were people like the Wright Brothers, Charles Lindbergh, and General Doolittle. There were others.

Harriet Quimby was one of them. In the early 1900's, she captured the imagination of men and women alike. She was America's darling. In her plane she looped and whirled through the air in a plum-colored flying suit. Quimby was the first woman in the United States to hold an airplane pilot's license. She was also the first woman to make a transatlantic flight. She flew across the English Channel.

She was not the only woman to take to the skies. One day a large balloon appeared over Little Falls, New York. In it was the first American woman to pilot this special type of aircraft. Her name was Mary Myers. She became a familiar sight at festivals. She delighted crowds as Carlotta, the Lady Aeronaut. In 1886, she did more than make local crowds gasp. She made the world gasp. Her gas-filled balloon went higher than any other balloon had gone before. She set a new world altitude record. This was a rather amazing feat. It was made without using any special breathing equipment.

On the West Coast women were active in flying, too. Georgia Broadwick was in the skies there. She was the first woman to parachute from an airplane. The drop was carried out over Griffith Park in Los Angeles.

Blanche Scott was also an aviation pioneer. Her path to the skies began in a car. She had been hired by the Willys Overland Company for a publicity stunt. She was to drive one of their cars from

Smithsonian Institution

Georgia Broadwick was the first woman to parachute from an airplane.

San Francisco to New York. She enjoyed her long drive Then she heard about even more exciting roads, sky roads. In Dayton, Ohio, she learned about the Wright Flying School. This was in 1910. Later that same year, she became the first woman to solo.

There were other woman pioneers. Side by side with men, they made those first glorious steps into space.

A. *Prefixes* are clues for understanding words. These clues are within the words themselves. They are found at the beginnings of words. Knowing their meanings can help you understand difficult words. Here are some common prefixes and their meanings. Use them to fill in the blanks below.

dis	often means	*not*
sub	often means	*under*
trans	often means	*across*
re	often means	*again*
inter	often means	*between*

1. *dishonest* means ---------------------------- honest
2. *substandard* means ---------------------------- standard
3. *transatlantic* means ---------------------------- Atlantic
4. *return* means turn ----------------------------
5. *interschool* means ---------------------------- schools

B. Choose one of the five words listed in Part A to complete each sentence below.

1. I don't want these tires because they are ----------------------------------.
2. The -- competitions involve all schools in the district.
3. We enjoyed your visit and hope you will ---.
4. It is -- to cheat on a test.
5. Jane is going from New York to England. Her flight is

   --.

C. Study the words below. Then write the prefix, the base word (the word the prefix is attached to), and the meaning of each word. The first one is done for you.

1. disliked
2. review
3. transport
4. submarine
5. international
6. subterranean
7. transoceanic
8. distasteful
9. renew
10. interoffice

	Prefix	Base Word	Meaning
1.	dis	liked	not liked, unpopular
2.	______	______	______
3.	______	______	______
4.	______	______	______
5.	______	______	______
6.	______	______	______
7.	______	______	______
8.	______	______	______
9.	______	______	______
10.	______	______	______

D. Prefixes can be added to form new words. Add the prefix in parentheses to the words below to form new words.

Base Word	New Word
1. continental (trans)	______
2. collegiate (inter)	______
3. agree (dis)	______
4. way (sub)	______
5. appoint (re)	______

An Olympian

In 1976, Jim Finch lost his legs in a car accident. He was 22 years old. Life seemed to be over for the young college student. Yet four years later he had won two gold medals, as well as a silver, and a bronze. The medals were won during the International Olympics for the Disabled.

The meet took place in Holland. More than 2,200 athletes participated. They came from 42 countries. Each event had several classes. Those with similar handicaps were grouped in the same class. Finch competed only against other double amputees.

Finch was proud of his success. "It's satisfying," he said. "But I'd still like to play a normal game of tennis. I'm one of those people who needs activity."

After his accident, Finch did not go right back into sports. It was hard for him to face a life without legs. He was often discouraged. He spent a year working with physical therapists. Then he was given the name of a man who played basketball in a league. That man was also a double amputee. "It took me ten months before I called him," Finch said. "But once I tried basketball, I found I enjoyed it."

One of his friends had been in the Boston Marathon. Finch decided to give that a try, too. Marathon racers need speed and endurance. Finch proved to himself that he had those qualities. He set about building a special chair to help him get around better on his own. The next step was to try out for the Olympic team. It was a series of victories after that.

Finch still has problems. He has come to terms with the hardest ones. Others may always remain.

Finch feels that there are more opportunities for the handicapped. These opportunities in jobs and in sports are important. They remind the handicapped that life is not over. They give the person something to look forward to. They make her or him want to try even harder.

Finch is looking forward to the next Olympic Games. He feels that they will be even more challenging. The athletes will be better.

A. Identify the prefix, the base word, and the meaning for each of the underlined words.

1. Jim won medals in the International Olympics.
2. Disabled athletes took part in the competition.
3. Jim was often discouraged.
4. Good job opportunities remind the handicapped that life is not over.

Prefix	Base Word	Meaning
1. ________	____________	______________________________
2. ________	____________	______________________________
3. ________	____________	______________________________
4. ________	____________	______________________________

B. The prefix *dis* often means not. Several other prefixes often have this same meaning. When added, they give the base word an opposite meaning. These prefixes are listed below. Make the words that follow into opposites by adding the appropriate prefix. The first one is done for you.

un non in im il or ill ir mis

1. mis behavior
2. ________ perfect
3. ________ fortune
4. ________ legal
5. ________ fit
6. ________ sense
7. ________ sane
8. ________ mortal
9. ________ regular
10. ________ stop

C. Use one of the new words in Part B to complete each sentence.

1. The stories told about the actor were lies. They were pure ____________________.
2. The teenagers hopped on one foot ____________________ for 24 hours in order to set a new world's record.
3. Five of the boys took apples from the tree. Only one had the ____________________ to be caught.
4. The judge told the troubled young man that he was ____________________ to be a father.
5. Driving without a license is ____________________.

An Unexpected Result

Fear can kill. One young lady didn't believe this. She sadly found out the hard way. Her death may help others to realize what too much fear can do.

Several years ago, Ellen's mother died of cancer. The death shattered Ellen. She hated the disease that killed her mother. She was also very afraid that the disease would kill her, too. No one could convince her that she did not have the disorder. She saw doctors at least ten times in a four-year period. Each time the doctors told her the same thing. She was perfectly healthy. There were no signs of a problem.

Her fears remained. She was certain that a cancer was growing inside her. She imagined it spreading poisons throughout her body. She felt the need to cleanse her body. Every few months, she went on a water diet. She ate no food at all when she dieted. She just drank lots of water. Each day she would drink 15 to 22 liters of water. The diet usually lasted around three weeks. It was her belief that this clear water would purify her system.

In February 1977 Ellen became severely ill. She was fasting at the time. Friends rushed her to the hospital. She died there from an overdose of drinking water. She was 29 years old. Her tremendous intake of water had damaged her cells. Their chemical balance was disturbed. They could no longer function properly. Finally the cells of her heart failed, too. They caused her heart to stop. Her fear of dying finally killed her.

The doctor commented: "This is one of the strangest cases I have ever seen. It's hard to kill yourself drinking water, but it can happen."

A. The word *psychosomatic* (si' ko so mat' ik) describes illnesses that are caused by the mind. The word itself is based upon *psycho*, meaning mind, and *soma*, meaning body.

Below is a list of words or word stems and their meanings. Add *psycho* to these as a prefix and give the meaning of the new word.

logy—the study of
pathic—a disorder
therapy—treatment

1. ____________________

2. ____________________

3. ____________________

B. Below is a list of prefixes and their meanings. At the right is a list of words. Add an appropriate prefix to each word to form a new word. The first is done for you.

Prefix	Meaning		Word
ex	out of, from	1.	**tele** vision
super	above	2.	______ sent
ab	away, from	3.	______ change
bi	two	4.	______ annual
semi	half	5.	______ motion
tele	at a distance	6.	______ structure
pro	for	7.	______ cycle
anti	against	8.	______ war

C. Use the prefixes listed in Part B to choose the best word to complete the following sentences. Circle the letter of the correct word.

1. That magazine comes every two months. The publication is
   a. semimonthly.
   b. bimonthly.
2. Those in the rally want to end all labor unions. They are
   a. prolabor.
   b. antilabor.
3. The king was forced to give up his throne. The people made him
   a. abdicate.
   b. indicate.
4. Some unpopular political leaders are forced to leave their land and live in other countries. They are
   a. expatriots.
   b. exporters.

Women's Lib

"I now pronounce you man and wife." These words mean marriage to many people. And these marriages involve one man and one woman. In some parts of the world, however, there are different customs. In some cultures, the harem is the accepted norm. A man living here may have more than one wife. In other places, an even rarer custom is practiced. Here the usual harem idea is reversed. One woman may have several husbands. The Berbers in Africa believe in this type of marriage. Queen Kahena of Aures, Algeria, had a harem of 400 males.

The reasons for these different marriage customs vary. In some societies there are too few women. In others men are scarce. In yet others women make up the ruling class.

Sometimes another type of unusual marriage occurs. This type has nothing to do with foreign cultures. Nor does it have anything to do with legal customs. It could happen anywhere. It happens when people just like to get married.

On December 19, 1922, an Englishwoman was brought to court. Her name was Therese Vaughn. She was 24 years old. The charge against her was that she had gotten married. She did so without bothering to divorce Mr. Vaughn.

At the hearing the police were in for a surprise! Mrs. Vaughn said that she had parted from her husband five years ago. Since then she had married 61 men! She had traveled in England, Germany, and South Africa. Most of her time was usually not spent in the common tourist spots. It was spent getting married. She had collected husbands at the rate of better than one a month!

A. The prefix *mono* means one. The prefix *poly* means many. Use this information to complete the sentences below. Circle the letter of the word that should go in each blank.

1. Most Americans believe in monogamous marriages. This means a person can have only ---------- husband or wife at a time.
   a. one
   b. many

2. There are very few places in the world where marriage is polygamous. This means people can have ---------- husbands or wives at a time.
   a. one
   b. many

3. Religions that believe in only one god are called ----------.

   a. monotheistic

   b. polytheistic

4. A single musical tone is called a ----------.

   a. monotone

   b. polytone

5. Words with several syllables are called ----------.

   a. monosyllables

   b. polysyllables

6. Carbon monoxide is gas. How many oxygen atoms does it have?

   ----

   a. one

   b. many

B. *Suffixes* provide more clues to understanding a word. They are the syllable or syllables added at the end of a base word. Two common suffixes are *y* and *ly*. Add *y* to the following words. Notice that it will change the base word from a noun to an adjective. The first one is done for you.

1. flower ----------flowery----------
2. water ------------------------------
3. rust ------------------------------
4. grass ------------------------------
5. lump ------------------------------
6. luck ------------------------------

C. Use the new words with suffixes in Part B in the following sentences.

1. The young carpenter tried to pull the -------------------- nail from the board.

2. The dog rolled down the -------------------- hill.

3. The hot oatmeal was --------------------, and the children did not eat it.

4. Mary was happy to find the horseshoe. She felt it was

------------------------.

5. The picnic came to a ------------------------ end when the thunderstorm struck.

6. Her ------------------------ dress was perfect for the summer party. It matched the real blooms outdoors.

I

D. Add *ly* to the following words. Notice that the new words will be adverbs. The first is done for you.

1. usual	usually	2. slow	------------------------
3. rapid	------------------------	4. loud	------------------------
5. quiet	------------------------	6. sweet	------------------------
7. proud	------------------------	8. cautious	------------------------

E. Use the new words in Part D to complete the following sentences.

1. The old man moved ------------------------ down the stairs.

2. The bird sang ------------------------.

3. The crowd danced and cheered as the om-pah band played

------------------------.

4. The thief ran ------------------------ away from the bank.

5. The little girls were ------------------------ dressed very neatly.

6. Father tiptoed ------------------------ into the room so that he would not wake the children.

7. He ------------------------ opened the door to the wild animals' cage.

8. I ------------------------ showed my best report card ever to my parents.

Grandma Is Building Space Satellites

Marie Marr is not a typical grandmother. She is 56 years old and studies space technology. She also builds satellites from scratch. She is finally doing what she had always wanted to do.

As a young girl she had planned to be an engineer. Her plans changed when her children came along. Their needs came first. She never completely shelved her dream. She just went after it differently. During World War II, she worked in electronics. Then in 1959, she went to work at the Goddard Space Center in Greenbelt, Maryland.

AMSAT Radio Amateur Satellite Corp.

At the Center, Marr worked on rockets and satellites. She worked there for twelve years. Then she applied for a new job. This job was with the Amateur Radio Corporation. They needed someone to build a small satellite. The satellite would be part of the OSCAR series. OSCAR stands for Orbiting Satellite Carrying Radio. OSCARs are used by ham radio operators throughout the world. Marr got the job.

An OSCAR is made out of wood and metal. Putting one together is somewhat like assembling a complex model airplane. A drop of glue is used here, a resistor put there, and a small tube placed somewhere else. Hundreds of parts are used. A battery provides the power. Everything is connected by wires. Marr calls the wiring "something like the arteries in the human body."

Making the OSCAR VI was not easy. Marr had to be quite resourceful. When the OSCAR VI was finished, it weighed less than 30 pounds. The real test was yet to come. It had to function in space. A Delta rocket carried it aloft. It went into orbit. Then it began relaying signals from amateur stations around the world. It was successful.

Ham operators rely on the OSCARs. Often the rest of the world does, too. During disasters, such as earthquakes and floods, normal radio channels may have been destroyed. In these emergencies, hams and OSCARs are there ready to help.

A. Match each word with its definition as used in the story. Write the correct letter in the blank.

----------	1. technology	a.	missile
----------	2. engineer	b.	in the air
----------	3. scratch	c.	nonprofessional
----------	4. rocket	d.	spacecraft that revolves around the earth
----------	5. satellite	e.	revolving path of a spacecraft around earth
----------	6. ham	f.	the study of applied science
----------	7. aloft	g.	a person who puts scientific knowledge to practical purpose
----------	8. orbit	h.	clever
----------	9. amateur	i.	the beginning
----------	10. resourceful	j.	amateur radio operators

B. Three suffixes change a word in the same way. When added to a base word, they change the word to mean the person who does or is expert in an activity. These suffixes are *er*, *or*, *ist*. Add *er* to the following base words. If the word ends in *e*, just add *r*. One is done for you.

Base Word	Active People
1. build	builder
2. teach	------------------------------
3. vote	------------------------------
4. trade	------------------------------
5. move	------------------------------
6. dance	------------------------------

C. Add *-or* to the following words. Then match the new word with its definition. Write the correct letter in the blank.

	Base Word	New Word	Definition
----------	1. act	------------------------------	a. a person who makes new things
----------	2. conduct	------------------------------	b. a person who rules
----------	3. invent	------------------------------	c. a person who appears in movies
----------	4. profess	------------------------------	d. a person who instructs
----------	5. govern	------------------------------	e. a person who works with orchestras

D. Add the suffix *ist* to the words below. Two words are done for you.

1. art ------------------------------
2. special ------------------------------
3. violin ------------------------------
4. machine machinist
5. piano pianist
6. balloon ------------------------------

E. Use five of the new words in Part D to correctly complete the following sentences.

1. The hands of the ------------------------------ seemed to dance on the ivory keys.
2. The ------------------------------ drilled many holes before he did anything else.
3. The doctor decided that another doctor's opinion was needed. She called in a ------------------------------.
4. The ------------------------------ painted a beautiful sunset.
5. Pilots fly airplanes, but there are also ------------------------------ who fly balloons filled with air.

Molasses Disaster

It sounds like a joke. To the people of Boston, it was no laughing matter. The Great Molasses Disaster was sweetness turned terribly sour. It was one of the most bizarre catastrophes of all time.

It began shortly after noon on January 15, 1919. Workers and residents on Boston's North Side heard several sharp explosions. A storage tank had blown up. The sharp sounds were followed by a rumble. Faces turned. Eyes saw, but people could not believe their eyes. An ocean of brown syrup was bearing down on everyone in its path. It was two stories high. The wave of sticky goo covered a two-block area. There was no escape. It left 21 dead and 150 injured. Countless homes and businesses were devastated.

The clean-up took many days. The cause was debated for years. Architects said one thing. Builders said another. Neither side had a "sweet victory." In fact, no one won. City engineers finally reported their findings. They concluded that both groups were responsible. The tank suffered from both poor design and faulty construction.

Courtesy of the Boston Public Library, Print Department

A. For each underlined word, identify the base word, the suffix, and the meaning of the word.

1. The disaster was sweetness turned <u>terribly</u> sour.
2. <u>Workers</u> and residents heard sharp explosions.
3. The wave of <u>sticky</u> goo covered a two-block area.
4. <u>Builders</u> said they weren't responsible.
5. The tank had poor design and <u>faulty</u> construction.

	Base Word	Suffix	Meaning
1.	----------------------	----------------	--
2.	----------------------	----------------	--
3.	----------------------	----------------	--
4.	----------------------	----------------	--
5.	----------------------	----------------	--

B. Below are six common suffixes and their meanings. Use them to figure out the meanings of the words that follow.

ful	means	*full of*
ment	means	*act or fact of*
able	means	*worthy of*
less	means	*lacking*
ness	means	*state or quality of*
ish	means	*acting like*

1. *careful* means --
2. *movement* means --
3. *remarkable* means --
4. *fearless* means --
5. *kindness* means --
6. *childish* means --

C. Use the words in Part B correctly in the following sentences.

1. The stranger's ------------------------------ will always be remembered.
2. For a first novel, the best-seller was ------------------------------.
3. That graceful ------------------------------ of the dancer was beautiful.
4. The children had to be ------------------------------ on the wet stones.
5. The girl was embarrassed by her sister's ------------------------------ behavior.
6. The mother cat was ------------------------------ in protecting her kittens.

Stalactites and Stalagmites

Sometimes the ground we walk on may not be as solid as it looks! Far beneath the earth's surface can be found huge, open areas. In some places they look like long, narrow tunnels. In other places they seem to be giant rooms. These are natural caves.

Caves occur mainly in limestone and chalk formations. These rocks are easily dissolved by water. Two types of stony deposits are found in caves. Stalactites hang like icicles from the roof of a cave. Stalagmites rise in columns and cones from the cave's floor. Both are formed when water acts on soft rock.

Water seeping down a cave's walls produces constant dripping. Each drop carries tiny limestone particles. The stone icicles form gradually. The word *stalactite* comes from a Greek word. It means "drop by drop."

Stalactites are hollow at first. The tiny limestone particles are on the outside of each drop of water. As the water evaporates, the hollow core slowly fills up. The deposit then becomes solid. Sometimes the deposit has the shape of one long icicle. Sometimes a hanging curtain of stone is formed. The curtain occurs when water drips from a long narrow cleft.

Faster flows of water may reach the floor of a cave. Here it builds up domes of stone. These stalagmites get larger with each new deposit of the limestone particles. In time, one might join a stalactite and form a column.

The tallest known stalagmite is located in France. It is about thirty meters high.

U.S. Department of the Interior

Stalactites and Stalagmites in Carlsbad Caverns

A. Prefixes and suffixes provide useful clues in unlocking the meaning of words. The base word or *root* can also provide clues. Often this root comes from other languages. Knowing where a root word comes from may help you understand its English meaning.

For each foreign word below, give at least one English word that comes from it.

1. *metron*—Greek for "measure" --
2. *arkhitekton*—Greek for "master builder" --
3. *autos*—Greek for "self" --
4. *kratos*—Greek for "rule, power" --
5. *batt*—Old English for "a club" --
6. *bord*—Old English for "a plank" --
7. *lytel*—Old English for "small" --
8. *hus*—Old English for "place of shelter" --

B. Use words derived from the foreign words in Part A to complete these sentences. Circle the letter of the correct word.

1. In the United States, the people have the final power. This type of government is a ----------.
   a. dictatorship
   b. democracy
2. I read an interesting --------- by one of the Supreme Court judges. He told his own life story.
   a. biography
   b. autobiography
3. The young boy loved to build. He dreamed one day of becoming an ----------.
   a. aristocrat
   b. architect

4. At the seashore, one of my greatest pleasures is to walk along the ---------- and watch the ocean—and the people!

   a. road

   b. boardwalk

5. That person takes care of our house. The person is a ----------.

   a. housekeeper

   b. guest

C. Many English words come from the Latin language. Match the English word in the left column with the Latin root in the right column. Write the correct letter in the blank.

---------- 1. arch

---------- 2. auction

---------- 3. fault

---------- 4. inflate

---------- 5. feast

---------- 6. gusto

---------- 7. infant

---------- 8. model

---------- 9. motion

----------10. description

a. *modulus*—little measurement

b. *festus*—joyous

c. *describere*—to tell about

d. *gustus*—taste

e. *arcus*—arc

f. *infans*—unable to talk

g. *fallere*—to fail

h. *inflare*—to blow into

i. *movere*—to move

j. *auctio*—a sale by bids

D. Use the words in Part C to complete the following sentences.

1. Before beginning construction, he built a ------------------------------ of the building.

2. After working hard all day, the farmer ate with ------------------------------.

3. They used an air pump to ------------------------------ the raft.

4. Jack's habit of chewing his nails was his only ------------------------------.

Ocean Tides

Ocean tides are controlled by the moon and the sun. The moon has the most influence because it is nearer the earth. The moon's position causes the tide to ebb and flow. Sometimes the sun and moon are directly in line. Then they combine to pull the earth's oceans in one direction. This is when the highest tides occur.

The tides affect the lives of small sea animals. Oysters, clams, and muscles must move with the tides. Some people think the tides affect humans, too. Certainly in California there is proof that the tides do affect both sea animals and—at least indirectly—humans, too. The grunion fish is native to California waters. It links its movements to the tide. When the tide is high and the moon is full, grunion "run." They hit the beaches to lay their eggs. The same high tide also brings out the people. They hit the beaches to watch the grunion run.

Steve Martin/Tom Stack & Associates

Grunion on Beach Sand

A. Ecology is the science that studies living things and their relation to each other and the world around them. The word *ecology* is made up of two parts, *eco* and *logy*. *Eco* comes from the Greek word for house, *oikos*. *Logy* comes from the Greek word *logos* and means science or study of.

What do the words below have in common?

Archeology
Meterology
Pathology
Sociology --

B. Look at the definitions of the parts of words below. Then answer the questions that follow. Use information from Part A to create the needed word.

astro	means	*outer space*
audio	means	*to hear*
bio	means	*life*
geo	means	*earth*
zoo	means	*animals*
psycho	means	*mind*
cardio	means	*heart*

1. What is the study of life? ------------------------------

2. What is the study of outer space? ------------------------------

3. A person who looks for oil would use which science?

   ----

4. A person who studies animal life would use which science?

   ----

5. A heart doctor would be a specialist in ------------------------------.

6. A ------------------------------ course would have content about the mind.

Grave Robbers

The past has always held a fascination for people. It is like a very old mirror that shows us what we were. Unhappily, more and more people want even more than self-knowledge from the past. They want instant cash. Since the 1970's, a terrible type of crime has been on the increase. The past is being destroyed. A number of ancient ruins have been dug up and ravaged.

In southwestern New Mexico, an ancient tribe used to live along the Rio Mimbres. Little is known about it. The tribe lived and died before other people explored the country. Some think that the tribe was gone hundreds of years before the Spanish came. Finding any trace of this ancient tribe is exciting. In time, the tribe's special brand of white pottery was discovered. In 1980 a single white bowl was worth $25,000. This pottery was found at 13 sites. Six of those sites were dug up illegally. Six others were bulldozed.

This same type of story is told throughout the West. The federal government owns a large site in Arizona. All finds here could have been preserved for all of us to enjoy. Instead looters were the ones to profit. They hauled

Robert C. Buitron

This 600-year-old cliff dwelling is in the Tonto National Forest in Arizona. The doorway on the left was broken out by vandals in order to steal artifacts from the ruin.

away hundreds of rare Indian artifacts. The art was worth $750,000. Burial mounds have been constantly raided.

"The big sites are almost all gone," says Scott Wood. Wood works near Phoenix. He is an archeologist. "It's very much like devastating New York and Washington, D.C."

One sad truth is that these thieves don't work alone. Some art dealers help them. They are willing to pay high prices for ancient art. These high prices serve to encourage theft. One New York dealer defends his undercover purchases. He says, "There's a fair chance that most of the pottery already on the market is at least of questionable legality."

Today there is a tough new law on the books. It has helped some. Many problems still remain. Those who guard the ancient treasures can't watch everyone. The territory is vast and rugged. Tracking thieves is very difficult.

Hopefully new ways will be found to guard our heritage. Meanwhile these ancient treasures, these secrets of our past, are being robbed. We all lose.

A. Choose the best answer to complete the following sentences. Circle the letter of your answer.

1. The past is like a mirror because it
   a. is very fragile.
   b. shows us a true reflection of what we were.
   c. gives only a partial picture.

2. A synonym for *self-knowledge* is
   a. autobiography.
   b. consciousness.
   c. self-awareness.

3. The word *unhappily* combines a root word with
   a. a suffix.
   b. a prefix.
   c. both a suffix and a prefix.

4. In the sentence, "A number of ancient ruins have been dug up and ravaged," the word *ravaged* means
   a. sold.
   b. destroyed.
   c. admired.

5. The word *archeologist* comes from the --------- language.
   a. Latin
   b. Greek
   c. Old English
6. The prefix *dis-* in *discover* means
   a. away from.
   b. not.
   c. in.
7. An antonym of *preserve* is
   a. destroy.
   b. maintain.
   c. keep.
8. A synonym for *devastating* is
   a. visiting.
   b. excavating.
   c. destroying.
9. The opposite of *encourage* is *discourage*. The meaning is changed by
   a. the suffix.
   b. the root word.
   c. the prefix.

B. *Compound words* are new words made by combining two separate words into one word. This can be a helpful clue for reading and spelling words. Put the two words together to make a new word for each blank. Then use the compound words in the sentences on page 72.

spring + time = ------------------------------------

deer + skin = ------------------------------------

wood + land = ------------------------------------

milk + weed = ------------------------------------

frame + work = ------------------------------------

1. The ______________________________ Indians made their homes in the thick woods.

2. They used young trees as the ______________________________ for their huts.

3. Much of their clothing was made of ______________________________.

4. The Indians could weave cloth from silk of the ______________________________.

5. Sometimes they drank the sweet sap from trees in the

______________________________.

C. Underline the compound words in the following sentences. Circle the best definition. The first one is marked.

1. Summer temperatures often reach 100° in the Southwest.
   a. an area that includes Maine, Massachusetts, and Vermont
   b. an area that includes Florida, Georgia, and Alabama
   (c.) an area that includes Arizona, Texas, and New Mexico

2. Burial grounds are often bulldozed for their treasure.
   a. dug out
   b. farmed
   c. known

3. Some art dealers made illegal purchases undercover.
   a. with the knowledge of the law
   b. secretly
   c. in disguise

4. The treasures on federal land belong to everybody.
   a. no one in particular
   b. all federal employees
   c. all people

5. Meanwhile the thefts go on.
   a. in the past
   b. at the same time
   c. in the future

For the Pet Owner Who Cares

It is said that anything can happen in New York. This may be true. A restaurant on Manhattan's East Side is certainly unique. It's called the Animal Gourmet. It caters only to cats and dogs. The menu is excellent. It compares well with those offered at some of New York's finest restaurants—those that serve people.

The menu has everything that the cat or dog on the town might want. It offers appetizers to begin with. These include shrimp cocktail or a liver paté. For the entree it will serve beef bourguignon, steak and kidney ragout, or braised chicken livers. Fish lovers may dine on poached fish filet. A special dish is Beef Wellington. The food served here is bought from the same suppliers used by regular restaurants.

The owners say that they sell three hundred or more meals a week. Their successful business began with their love for their own animals. They hated to give their pets canned food. Now the sign at the entrance reads: "We do not prepare dog and cat food. We prepare food for dogs and cats." Meals are served at small white tables with white tablecloths. The beverage of the day is always water.

Animal Gourmet also offers birthday parties for animals. They ask to have advance notice. Then they provide flowers, a band, and a birthday cake. The cake is made of dry meal, liver, whipped milk, and cream.

The place has served the two pugs owned by the Duchess of Windsor for many years. It has a guest list which includes the dogs and cats of many famous people.

A. Some people would say that taking a dog to a restaurant for dinner is *extravagant*. This means that it is an expense that is *beyond* what people would ordinarily agree to. Many English words have the Latin word *extra* used as a prefix. *Extra* means outside or beyond. Redefine each word below to show its meaning when *extra* is added.

1. If cellular means having to do with the cells in a body, then *extracellular* means --.

2. If galactic means being from a part of the Milky Way Galaxy, then *extragalactic* means --.

3. If legal means having to do with the law, then *extralegal* means --.

4. If ordinary means typical, then *extraordinary* means

--.

5. If sensory means the five senses are involved, then *extrasensory* means --.

B. Match the following words with their definitions as used in the story. Write the letter of the correct definition in the blank.

---------- 1. unique	a. main course
---------- 2. gourmet	b. beginning course
---------- 3. cater	c. one of a kind
---------- 4. entree	d. prior
---------- 5. advance	e. an expert on fine food
---------- 6. appetizer	f. provide service

C. Below are two lists of words. Combine a word from Column 1 with a word in Column 2 to form a new word. Write the new words in the blanks below.

Column 1	Column 2
any	fly
birth	bow
rain	thing
butter	day
pocket	book
common	ship
battle	place

1. -- 2. --

3. -- 4. --

5. -- 6. --

7. --

Review

A. ***Synonyms*** **are words that have the same or nearly the same meaning. An example of two synonyms would be *often* and *frequently*. In various exercises, synonyms were required for these words. See if you still know synonyms for them.**

1. battle ______________ 2. huge ______________

3. tired ______________ 4. dawn ______________

5. identical ______________ 6. crucial ______________

7. gear ______________ 8. gather ______________

9. formerly ______________ 10. stop ______________

B. ***Antonyms*** **are words that have the opposite or nearly the opposite meaning. An example of two antonyms would be *true* and *false*. In earlier exercises, antonyms were required for these words. Test your memory to see if you still know them.**

1. ancient ______________ 2. energetic ______________

3. ordinary ______________ 4. weakness ______________

5. lasting ______________ 6. forbidden ______________

7. preserve ______________ 8. precious ______________

C. ***Homonyms*** **are words that sound alike but are spelled differently. An example of two homonyms would be *hear* and *here*. The following homonyms were used in various exercises. Can you still complete the homonym pair?**

1. won ______________ 2. red ______________

3. pail ______________ 4. weigh ______________

5. days ______________ 6. right ______________

7. here ______________ 8. kneed ______________

D. ***Brainstorming*** **on groups of related words means trying to think of a number of words on a given subject. The results are often surprising. You may know more words than you thought you did. Two of the subjects in earlier lessons were horses and things with the word *wood* in them. Can you still come up with 5 words for each subject?**

horses	"woody" things
----------	----------
----------	----------
----------	----------
----------	----------
----------	----------

E. Within a word itself are clues to meaning. Sometimes being able to break a difficult word into smaller parts makes it easier to understand. Words can be broken into *prefixes, suffixes,* and *root words.*

Prefixes **are the syllable or syllables that come before root words. They have definite meanings. For example, *mono* is a prefix that means one. The word *monotone,* therefore, means one tone. You have worked with several prefixes. Write the meaning of each underlined prefix.**

1. immortal ----------
2. irrelevant ----------
3. misbehave ----------
4. television ----------
5. superman ----------
6. transatlantic ----------

F. ***Suffixes*** **are the syllable or syllables added to the end of root words. They have meanings also. The suffix *ful,* for example, means full of. The word *careful,* therefore, means full of care. Write the meaning of each underlined suffix.**

1. teacher ----------
2. conductor ----------
3. violinist ----------
4. kindness ----------
5. thoughtless ----------
6. softly ----------